What *Jazz 'n' Blues* Can I Pl
Flute
Grades One, Two & Three

Series Editors: Mark Mumford and Tim Siddall

Music arranged and processed by
Barnes Music Engraving Ltd
East Sussex TN22 4HA, England

Published 1996

Introduction

In this *What Jazz 'n' Blues Can I Play?* collection you'll find twelve popular tunes that are both challenging and entertaining.

The pieces have been carefully selected and arranged to provide a fascinating introduction to jazz and blues, and are ideal for young flautists who are either working towards or have recently taken a Grade One, Two or Three flute examination.

Technical demands increase progressively, gradually introducing new concepts, and each piece offers suggestions and guidelines on breathing, dynamics and tempo, together with technical tips and performance notes.

Whether it's for light relief from examination preparation, or to reinforce the understanding of new concepts, this collection will enthuse and encourage all young flute players.

Note: references to fingering within this book use Thumb 1 2 3 4.

Jeepers creepers

Words by Johnny Mercer, Music by Harry Warren

When the Saints go marching in

Traditional

Down hearted blues

Words and Music by Alberta Hunter and Louie Austin

Five foot two, eyes of blue
(Has anybody seen my girl?)

Words by Joe Young and Sam Lewis, Music by Ray Henderson

Blueberry Hill

Words and Music by Al Lewis, Larry Stock and Vincent Rose

Sentimental journey

Words and Music by Bud Green, Les Brown and Ben Homer

Pennsylvania 6-5000

By Carl Sigman and Jerry Gray

U.F.O. blues

Words by Tom Stanier, Music by Jim Parker

Black bottom

Words by Lew Brown and Buddy De-Sylva, Music by Ray Henderson

Blue moon

Words by Lorenz Hart, Music by Richard Rodgers

Satin doll

Words and Music by Billy Strayhorn, Duke Ellington and Johnny Mercer

Little brown jug

Traditional

Reproduced and printed by Halstan & Co. Ltd., Amersham, Bucks., England